50p

GOD IS...

Available from March 1991:

Gaberdine Swine   Roy Mitchell

*Roy Mitchell regularly contributes
'Gaberdine Swine' – a well-loved cartoon
strip – to the magazine 21st Century
Christian.*

GOD IS...

Theology
for cats
and other
creatures

Cartoons by **Roy Mitchell**

MARSHALL·PICKERING

William Collins Sons & Co. Ltd
London · Glasgow · Sydney · Auckland
Toronto · Johannesburg

First published in Great Britain in 1990 by Marshall Pickering

Marshall Pickering is an imprint of
Collins Religious Division,
part of the Collins Publishing Group
8 Grafton Street, London W1X 3LA

Printed and bound in Great Britain by
Cox & Wyman Ltd, Reading, Berks

Acknowledgments

With thanks to friends at Holy Trinity and Christ Church, Stalybridge, and with especial thanks to Veronica, for her support and critical appraisal.

GOD IS....

...NOT PUT OFF BY APPEARANCES

GOD IS......

... NOT A TRIVIAL
PURSUIT

GOD IS...

... MORE PATIENT WITH US THAN **WE ARE**

GOD IS......

... A GREAT GARDENER

GOD IS...

...LONGING TO HEAR FROM YOU

GOD IS....

...THE WIND IN
MY SAILS

GOD IS.....

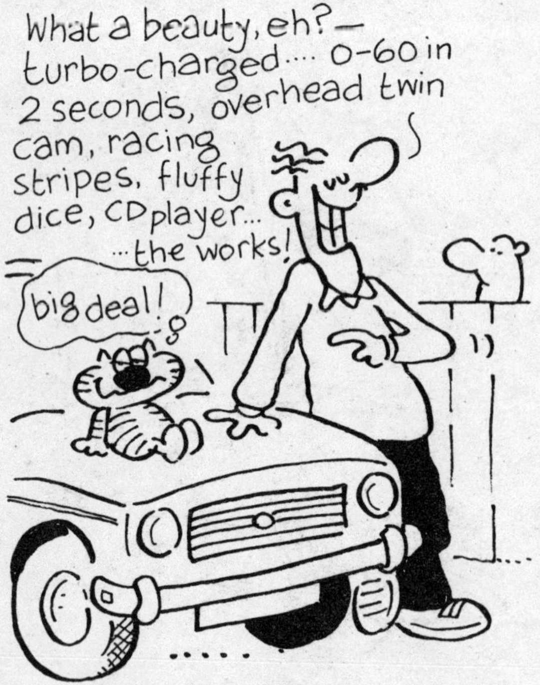

... NOT HAPPY TO PLAY SECOND FIDDLE

GOD IS....

...ALWAYS READY TO FORGIVE

GOD IS....

...ALWAYS ON TIME

GOD IS......

...COLOUR BLIND

GOD IS....

...MY PRESCRIPTION FOR **LIFE**

GOD IS....

GOD IS...

...ABLE TO TAKE
THE STRAIN

GOD IS......

... NEVER TOO BUSY
TO LISTEN

GOD IS....

...**NEVER** BORING

GOD IS......

...MY EVERY STEP

GOD IS....

Oh, Lord, if I may deign to speak with thee, I do hereby beseech thee... ...thy most humble and unworthy servant... waffle... waffle...

I wish he'd get to the point!

...NOT IMPRESSED BY WAFFLE

GOD IS....

...WANTING TO SPEAK
TO YOU

GOD IS....

... MY CO-PILOT

GOD IS...

...MAN'S (AND WOMAN'S!) BEST FRIEND

GOD IS....

...THE BEST THING BEFORE (AND SINCE) SLICED BREAD

GOD IS....

...NOT EXCLUSIVE

GOD IS....

... **ALWAYS** IN STYLE

GOD IS......

GOD IS...

... DELIGHTED BY OUR PRAISE

GOD IS......

Church? – oh, yes, I go every Christmas, and Easter... and to weddings... oh, and funerals, of course...

...LOOKING FOR **FULL-TIME** FOLLOWERS

GOD IS......

GOD IS....

...A FULLY-QUALIFIED
INSTRUCTOR

GOD IS........

I've got to get through all this lot today... but I don't like to bother you... I know you've got more important things to do... So don't worry, forget it... I'll manage it myself... somehow...

the 'phone's ringing!

...CAPABLE

GOD IS...

...MY FORTRESS

GOD IS...

... A TOWER OF
STRENGTH

GOD IS....

...FOR WORDS

GOD IS...

...NOT AFFECTED BY MONDAY MORNINGS

GOD IS...

... NOT DEAF

GOD IS....

...SOMETIMES THE **LAST** TO BE INVOLVED

GOD IS......

... ABLE TO **KEEP** A SECRET

GOD IS...

... PERMANENT

GOD IS...

...OPEN ALL HOURS

Now that's what I call Service!

GOD IS....

...THE LIGHT OF MY LIFE

GOD IS......

...READY TO PICK
YOU UP

even when
you're
clumsy!

GOD IS....

...UNSHOCKABLE

GOD IS......

No, I just don't want to get involved...

... NOT HAPPY TO BE KEPT AT ARM'S LENGTH

GOD IS...

...WILLING (AND ABLE) TO CHANGE YOU

GOD IS...

... NOT AN OGRE

GOD IS....

...THE **MASTER** POTTER

GOD IS...

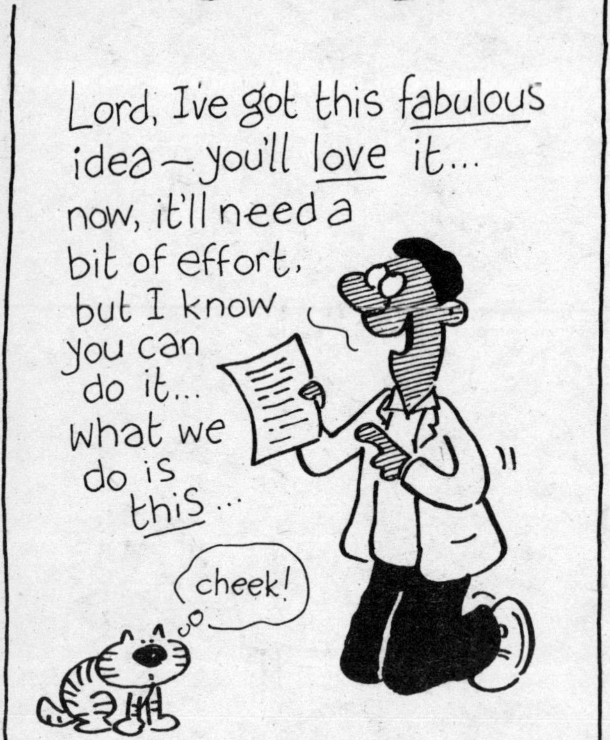

...WELL ABLE TO MAKE HIS OWN PLANS

GOD IS...

...THE INSPIRATION IN OUR PERSPIRATION

GOD IS....

cat burglar

...NOT **ALWAYS** ON ON OUR SIDE

GOD IS...

...TOO BIG TO FIT
IN A BOX

GOD IS....

... NOT ON
REMOTE CONTROL

GOD IS......

... MY SHIELD AND
DEFENDER

GOD IS...

GOD IS........

... THE GREATEST
EVER LIVING ARTIST

GOD IS...

... ALL-KNOWING

GOD IS...

...SOLID ROCK
BENEATH MY FEET

GOD IS...

... THERE AT OUR COMING IN...

GOD IS...

... AND OUR GOING
OUT

GOD IS...

...SLOW TO ANGER

GOD IS...

...NEVER ENGAGED

GOD IS...

...SOMETIMES SAD

GOD IS...

Last week's number one, down three places...

...**ALWAYS** NUMBER ONE

GOD IS....

...WORTH STUDYING

GOD IS....

...ANCIENT AND MODERN

GOD IS.....

... THE GREATEST EVER
HEART SURGEON

GOD IS....

...ALL SEEING

GOD IS....

... SMARTER THAN
ANY COMPUTER

GOD IS....

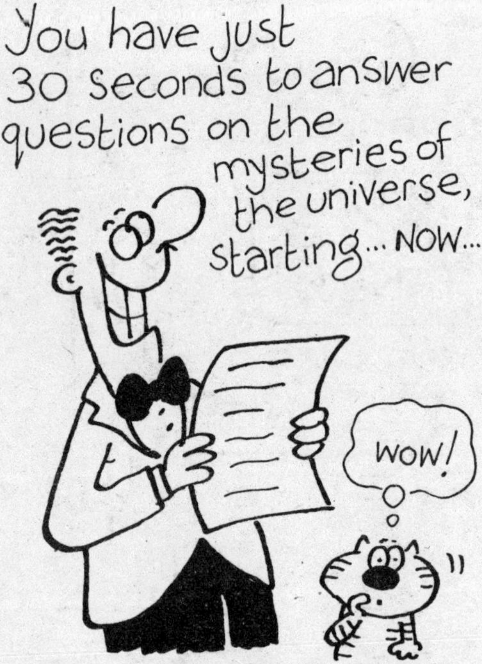

...THE ONLY KNOW-ALL WHO REALLY **DOES**

GOD IS...

...THE BEGINNING **AND** THE END

GOD IS....

...MY LIFE-SAVER

GOD IS....

...THE ONLY HERO WHO'S **WORTH** WORSHIPPING

GOD IS......

...WANTING TO COME INTO YOUR LIFE

GOD IS....

... THE POSITIVE TO OUR NEGATIVE

GOD IS....

...OUR CREATOR

GOD IS......

...MY REFRESHMENT

GOD IS....

...MORE THAN A CRUTCH

...he's the complete life-support system!

GOD IS....

... NOT LIKE
SANTA CLAUS

GOD IS...

The RIGHT TRACK

...A RELIABLE GUIDE

GOD IS...

...NON-DENOMINATIONAL

GOD IS...

...THE CAKE **AND** THE ICING

GOD IS....

... INCORRUPTIBLE

GOD IS....

...GOOD NEWS ON A DREARY DAY

GOD IS......

... GOOD NEWS ON **ANY** DAY!

GOD IS....

...AN OPEN DOOR

GOD IS...

...OVER THE WEATHER

GOD IS......

... NOT A DEMOCRAT

GOD IS...

...THERE WHEN
NOBODY ELSE IS

GOD IS...

... A SHOULDER TO CRY ON

GOD IS....

... WORTH A MILLION
AGONY AUNTS

GOD IS...

I wanted to
Send him a
Birthday card!

...AGELESS

GOD IS......

... NOT INTERESTED IN PERFORMANCES

GOD IS....

...NOT WORRIED WHEN
WE SING OFF-KEY

GOD IS...

... THE LAST WORD

GOD IS......

... FIGHTING FIT

GOD IS....

... **NEVER** ASLEEP

GOD IS......

...ABLE TO CARRY
YOUR BURDENS

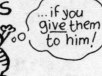

...if you
give them
to him!

GOD IS......

Now, in **my** opinion,
I reckon that
what the Lord
wants is....

No, you're wrong—
I think that
what he wants is...

..You're **both**
wrong—take
my word for it,
what he
really
wants is...

?!??

... WANTING TO GET A
WORD IN EDGEWAYS

GOD IS....

...THE POWER FOR HIS PEOPLE

GOD IS...

...a pinch of peace, a jug of joy...

...and a lot of love!

...THE MAIN INGREDIENT

GOD IS....

...THE ROCK THAT DOESN'T ROLL

GOD IS......

...HIGH AND
MIGHTY

GOD IS......

...NOT A SPOILSPORT

GOD IS....

...my future!

GOD IS....

... NEVER LATE FOR WORK

GOD IS...

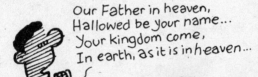

Our Father in heaven,
Hallowed be your name...
Your kingdom come,
In earth, as it is in heaven...

...wie in Himmel
also auch auf Erde...
Unser tägliche Brot
gib uns heute.....

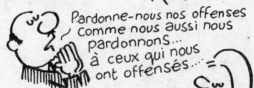

Pardonne-nous nos offenses
Comme nous aussi nous
pardonnons...
à ceux qui nous
ont offensés...

...Y no nos metas en
tentaciòn... sino libranos
del maligno.. Que tuyo
es el reino el poder
y la gloria...

...for ever and ever... Amen.

...MULTILINGUAL

GOD IS....

... THE GREATEST
EVER LIVING AUTHOR

GOD IS......

'Course I fiddle my expenses... Well, it's not really cheating, is it? — anyway, doesn't everybody do it? — and does it really matter? — in a way, it's expected of me... and the company can afford it, can't they?

...NOT INTERESTED IN EXCUSES

GOD IS...

... TO BE TAKEN SERIOUSLY

GOD IS....

... COMMITTED TO US

GOD...

GOD IS......

...FOR EVER,
and EVER,
and EVER, and
EVER, and EVER,
and EVER and
EVER, and EVER...

...Amen!